ED EMBERLEY'S DRAWING BOOK

MAKE A WORLD

LITTLE, BROWN
AND COMPANY
BOSTON—TORONTO

THIS BOOK WILL SHOW YOU
HOW TO DRAW ENOUGH THINGS
TO MAKE A WORLD OF YOUR OWN.

I HOPE YOU WILL TRY THIS WAY,
CONTINUE TO DRAW YOUR OWN WAY,
AND KEEP LOOKING FOR NEW WAYS—
I DO.

Happy Drawing!

Ed Emberley

IF YOU CAN DRAW THESE THINGS⟶
YOU CAN DRAW ALL THE OBJECTS
IN THIS BOOK. FOR, INSTANCE:
YOU USE THESE
TO MAKE THIS FISH
   THE DIAGRAMS ON THE
FOLLOWING PAGES WILL SHOW
   YOU HOW.

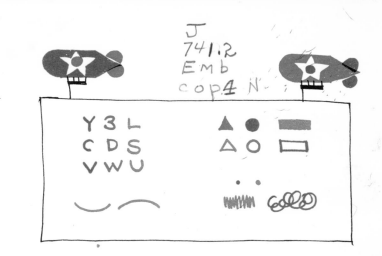

OTHER BOOKS BY ED EMBERLEY:
THE WING ON A FLEA
THE PARADE BOOK
ROSEBUD
PUNCH AND JUDY
LONDON BRIDGE IS FALLING DOWN
GREEN SAYS GO
ED EMBERLEY'S DRAWING BOOK OF ANIMALS

THE ARTWORK FOR THIS
BOOK WAS DRAWN ON
STRATHMORE PAPER
WITH FELT TIP AND
RAPIDOGRAPH PENS,
FOUR-COLOR, PRESEPARATED
AND HAND-LETTERED
BY THE AUTHOR.

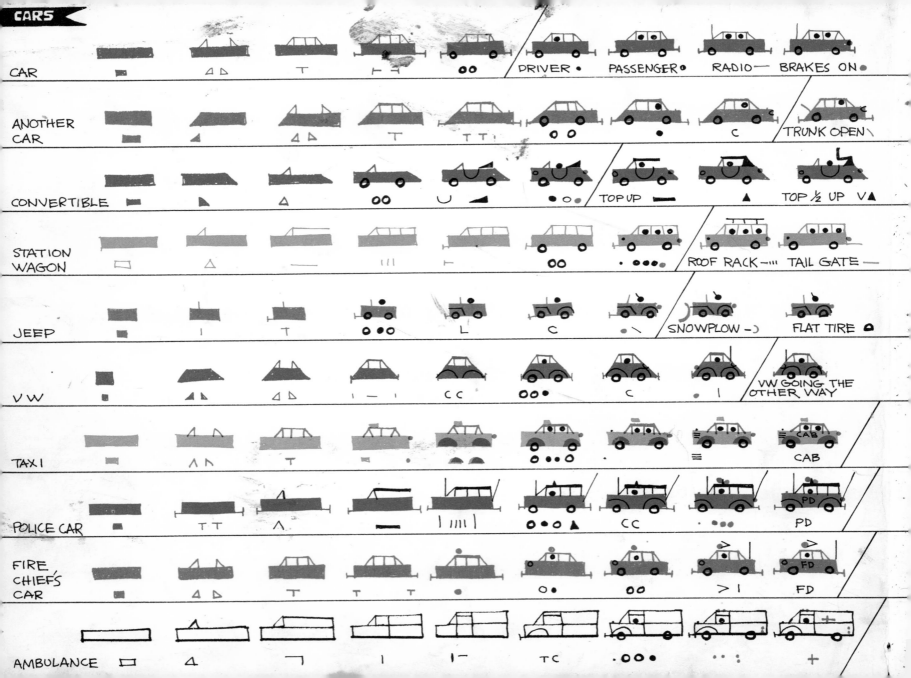

CARS

CAR — | △ ▷ | T | T⊢ | ∘∘ | DRIVER • | PASSENGER • | RADIO — | BRAKES ON •

ANOTHER CAR — | ▲ | △ ▷ | T | TT⊢ | ∘∘ | • | C | TRUNK OPEN ╲

CONVERTIBLE ▬ | ◣ | △ | ∘∘ | ∪ ◢ | • ∘• | TOP UP ▬ | ▲ | TOP ½ UP ∨▲

STATION WAGON ▭ | △ | — | ⫼ | ⊢ | ∘∘ | • ••• | ROOF RACK ⫼ | TAIL GATE —

JEEP ▭ | I | T | ∘∘∘ | L | C | • ╲ | SNOWPLOW ⟩ | FLAT TIRE ⬭

VW ▪ | ▲▲ | △ ▷ | I — I | C C | ∘∘• | C | • I | VW GOING THE OTHER WAY

TAXI ▭ | ∧ ∧ | T | ▬ | ⌣⌣ | ∘ •∘ | | ≡ | CAB

POLICE CAR ▪ | T T | ∧ | ▬ | I ⫼ I | ∘ •∘ ▲ | C C | • •• | PD

FIRE CHIEF'S CAR ▪ | △ ▷ | T | T T | • | ∘• | ∘∘ | ⟩ I | FD

AMBULANCE ▱ | △ | ⌐ | I | I— | T C | •∘∘• | ••• ⋮ | +

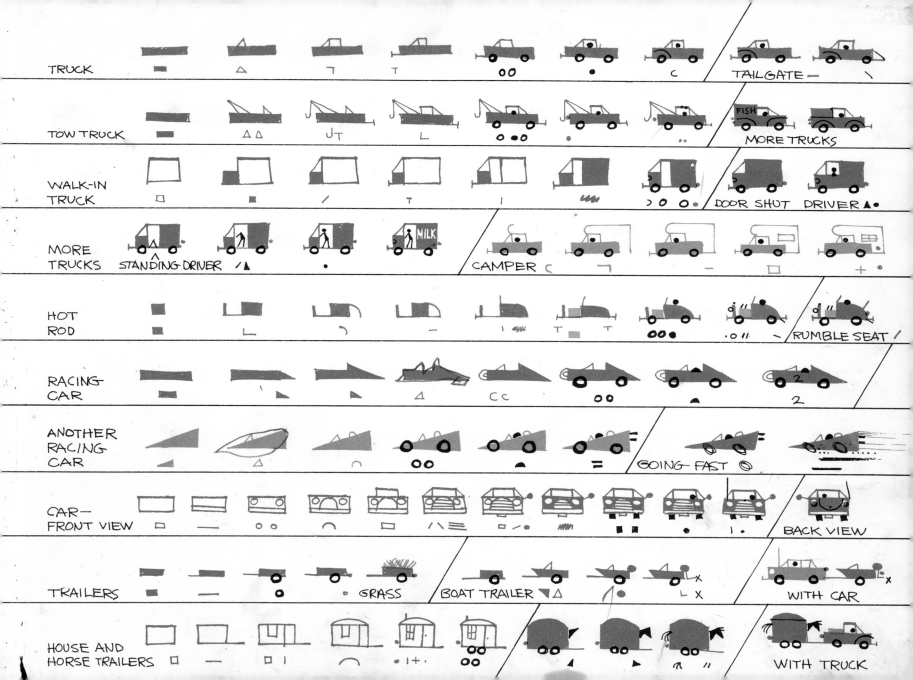

TRUCK

TAILGATE —

TOW TRUCK

FISH   MORE TRUCKS

WALK-IN
TRUCK

DOOR SHUT   DRIVER

MORE
TRUCKS   STANDING DRIVER   MILK   CAMPER

HOT
ROD   RUMBLE SEAT

RACING
CAR

ANOTHER
RACING
CAR   GOING FAST

CAR—
FRONT VIEW   BACK VIEW

TRAILERS   GRASS   BOAT TRAILER   WITH CAR

HOUSE AND
HORSE TRAILERS   WITH TRUCK

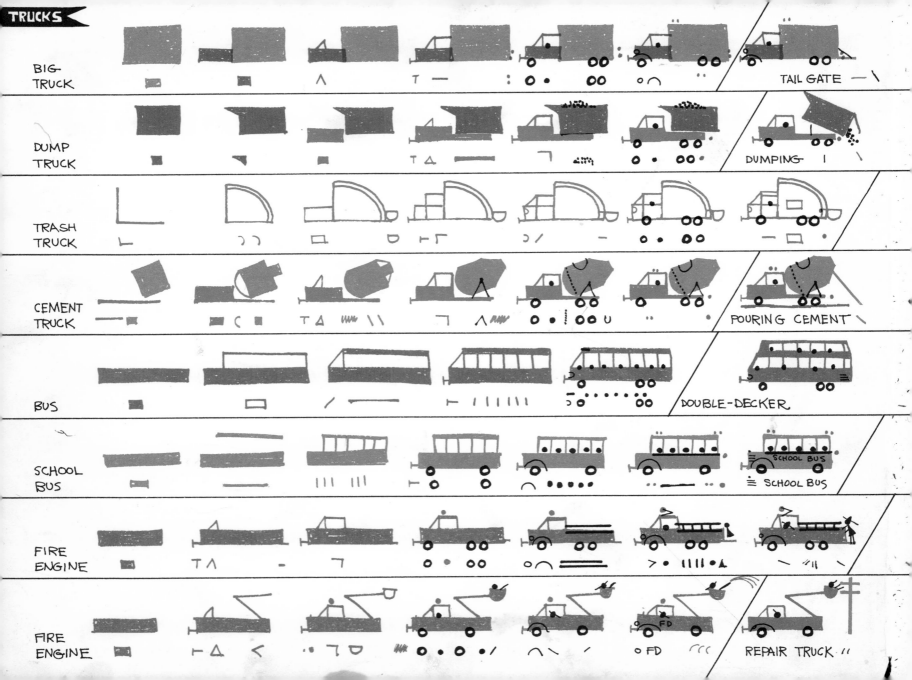

TRUCKS

BIG TRUCK — TAIL GATE

DUMP TRUCK — DUMPING

TRASH TRUCK

CEMENT TRUCK — POURING CEMENT

BUS — DOUBLE-DECKER

SCHOOL BUS — SCHOOL BUS

FIRE ENGINE

FIRE ENGINE — REPAIR TRUCK

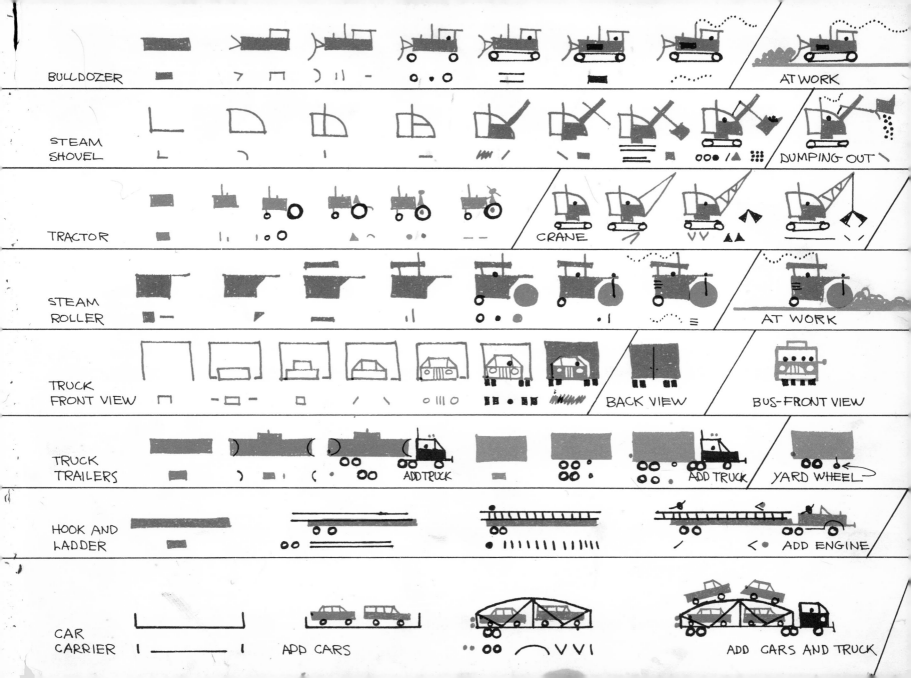

BULLDOZER · AT WORK

STEAM SHOVEL · DUMPING OUT

TRACTOR · CRANE

STEAM ROLLER · AT WORK

TRUCK FRONT VIEW · BACK VIEW · BUS-FRONT VIEW

TRUCK TRAILERS · ADD TRUCK · ADD TRUCK · YARD WHEEL

HOOK AND LADDER · ADD ENGINE

CAR CARRIER · ADD CARS · ADD CARS AND TRUCK

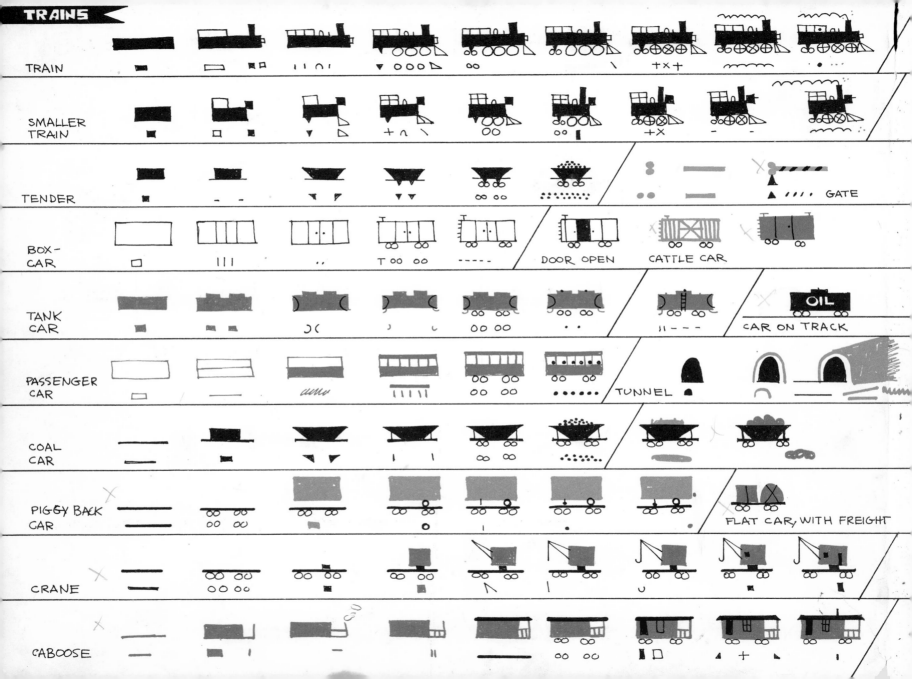

TRAINS

TRAIN

SMALLER TRAIN

TENDER

GATE

BOX-CAR

DOOR OPEN   CATTLE CAR

TANK CAR

CAR ON TRACK

PASSENGER CAR

TUNNEL

COAL CAR

PIGGY BACK CAR

FLAT CAR, WITH FREIGHT

CRANE

CABOOSE

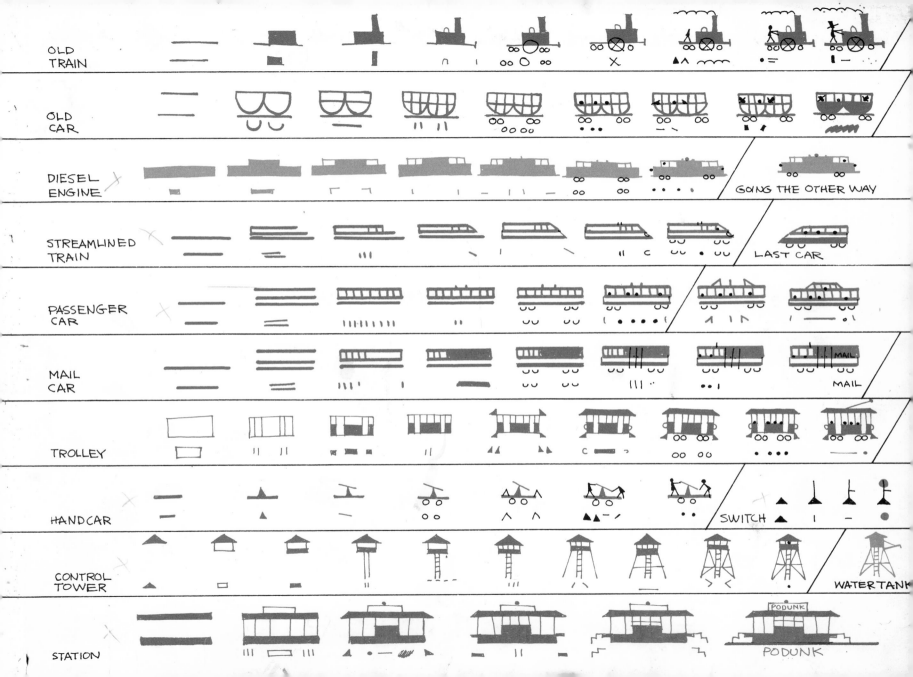

OLD TRAIN

OLD CAR

DIESEL ENGINE — GOING THE OTHER WAY

STREAMLINED TRAIN — LAST CAR

PASSENGER CAR

MAIL CAR — MAIL

TROLLEY

HANDCAR — SWITCH

CONTROL TOWER — WATER TANK

STATION — PODUNK

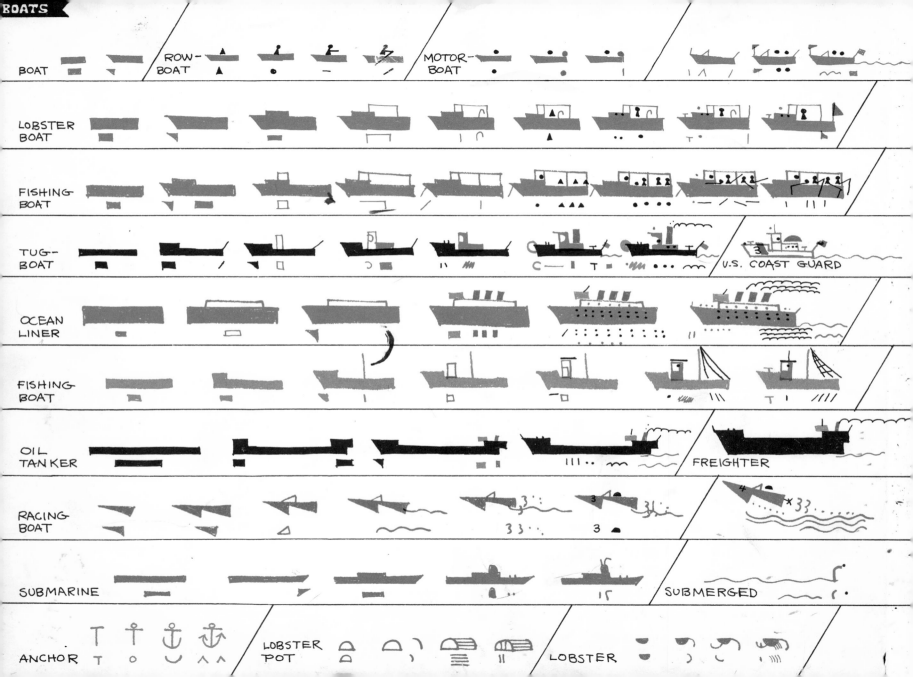

BOATS

BOAT

ROW-BOAT   MOTOR-BOAT

LOBSTER BOAT

FISHING BOAT

TUG-BOAT   U.S. COAST GUARD

OCEAN LINER

FISHING BOAT

OIL TANKER   FREIGHTER

RACING BOAT

SUBMARINE   SUBMERGED

ANCHOR   LOBSTER POT   LOBSTER

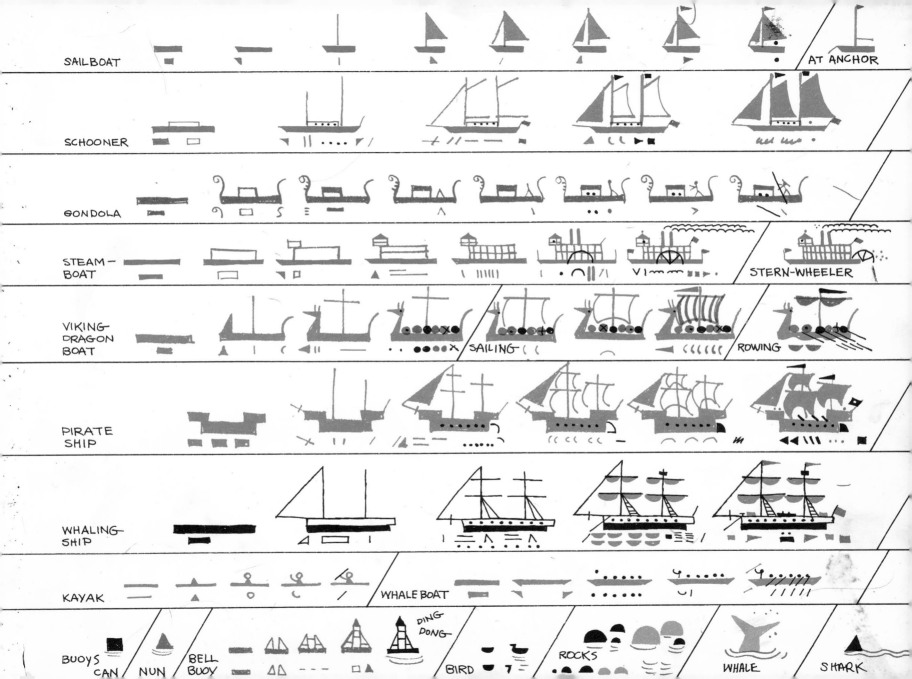

SAILBOAT

AT ANCHOR

SCHOONER

GONDOLA

STEAM-BOAT

STERN-WHEELER

VIKING DRAGON BOAT

SAILING

ROWING

PIRATE SHIP

WHALING SHIP

KAYAK

WHALE BOAT

BUOYS CAN NUN BELL BUOY DING DONG BIRD ROCKS WHALE SHARK

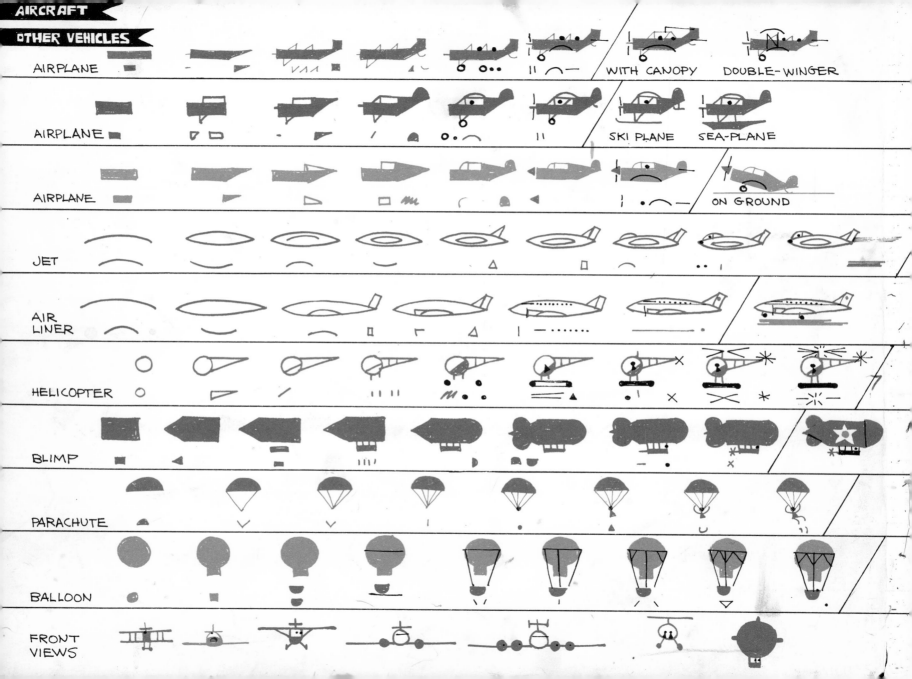

AIRCRAFT

OTHER VEHICLES

AIRPLANE — WITH CANOPY   DOUBLE-WINGER

AIRPLANE — SKI PLANE   SEA-PLANE

AIRPLANE — ON GROUND

JET

AIR LINER

HELICOPTER

BLIMP

PARACHUTE

BALLOON

FRONT VIEWS

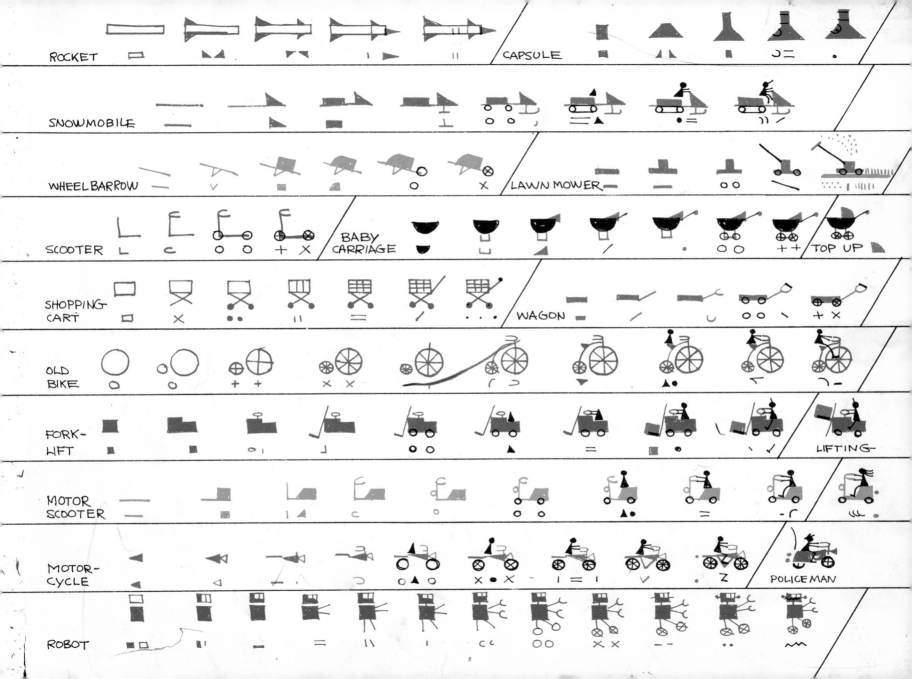

ROCKET

CAPSULE

SNOWMOBILE

WHEELBARROW

LAWN MOWER

SCOOTER

BABY CARRIAGE

TOP UP

SHOPPING CART

WAGON

OLD BIKE

FORK-LIFT

LIFTING

MOTOR SCOOTER

MOTOR-CYCLE

POLICE MAN

ROBOT

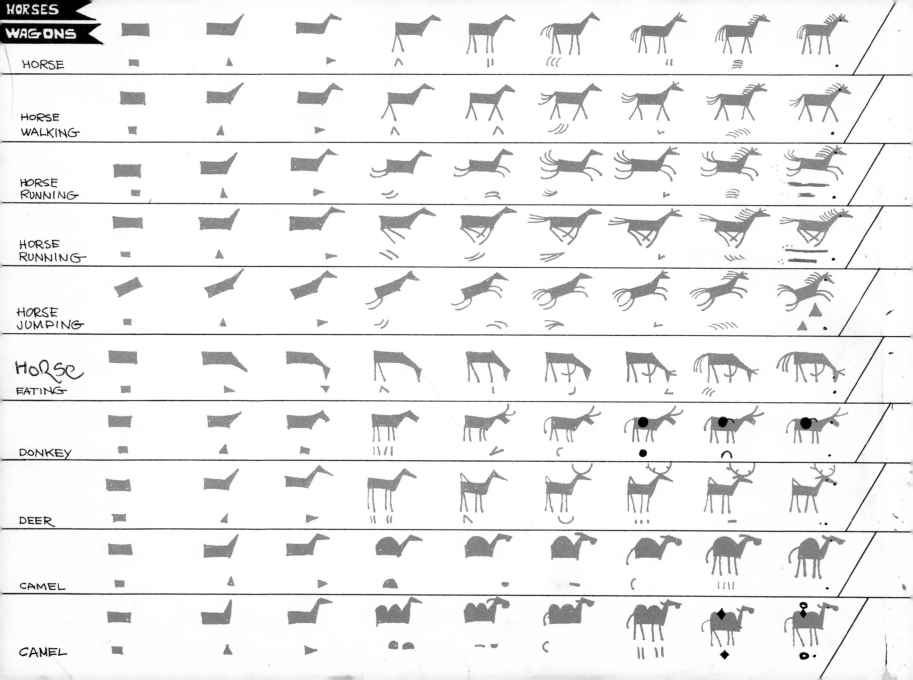

HORSE

HORSE WALKING

HORSE RUNNING

HORSE RUNNING

HORSE JUMPING

HORSE EATING

DONKEY

DEER

CAMEL

CAMEL

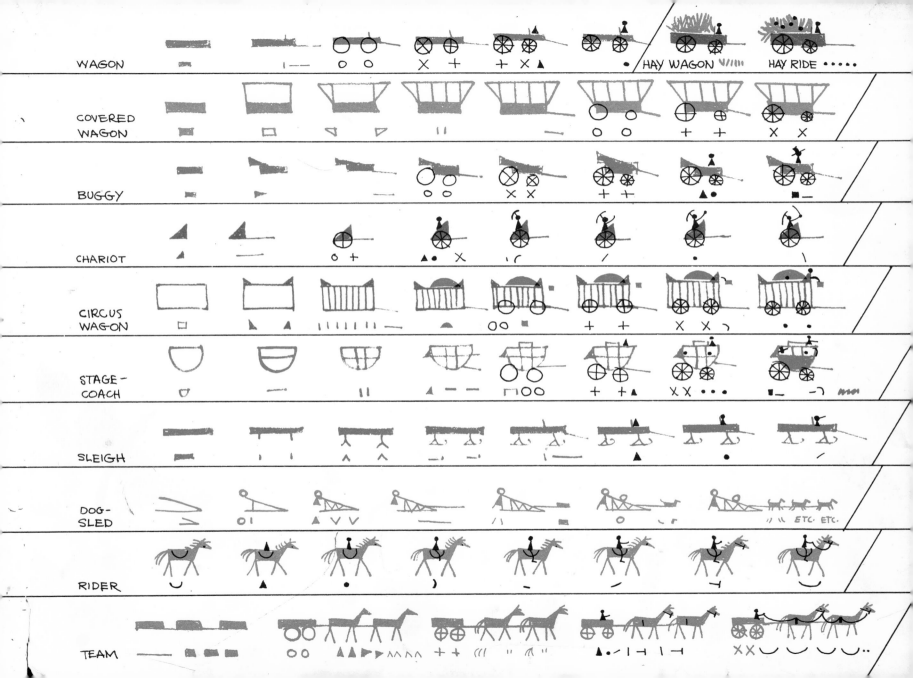

WAGON

COVERED WAGON

BUGGY

CHARIOT

CIRCUS WAGON

STAGE-COACH

SLEIGH

DOG-SLED

RIDER

TEAM

HAY WAGON   HAY RIDE

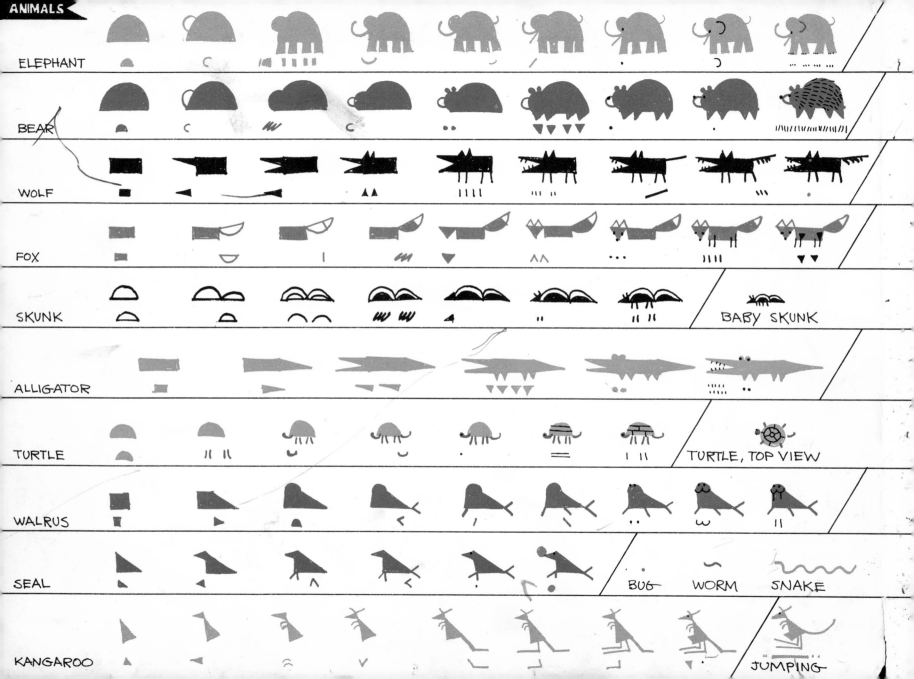

ANIMALS

ELEPHANT

BEAR

WOLF

FOX

SKUNK

BABY SKUNK

ALLIGATOR

TURTLE

TURTLE, TOP VIEW

WALRUS

SEAL

BUG   WORM   SNAKE

KANGAROO

JUMPING

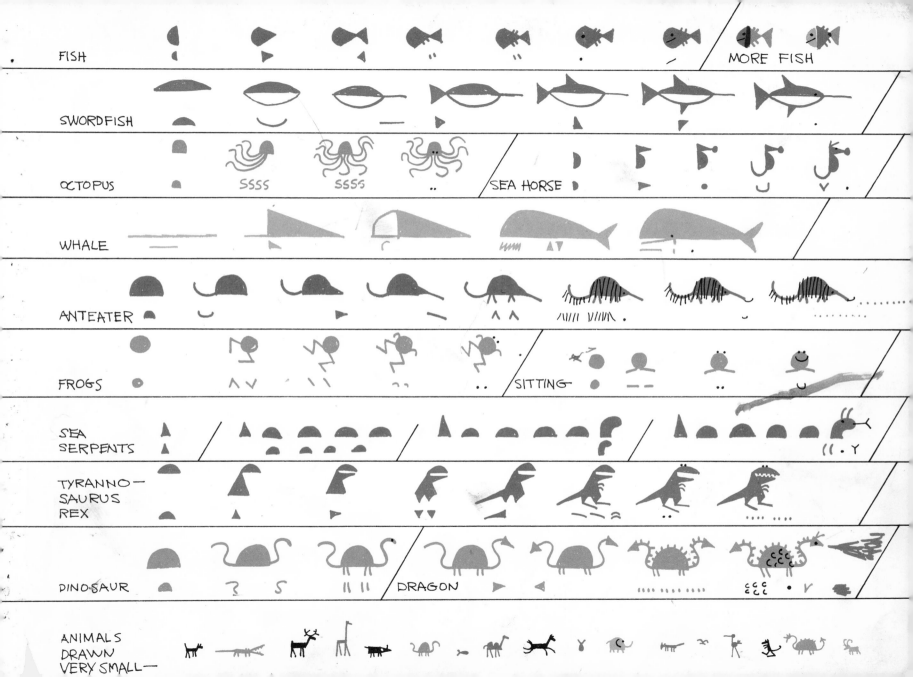

FISH

MORE FISH

SWORDFISH

OCTOPUS

SSSS

SSSS

SEA HORSE

WHALE

ANTEATER

FROGS

SITTING

SEA
SERPENTS

TYRANNO—
SAURUS
REX

DINOSAUR

DRAGON

ANIMALS
DRAWN
VERY SMALL—

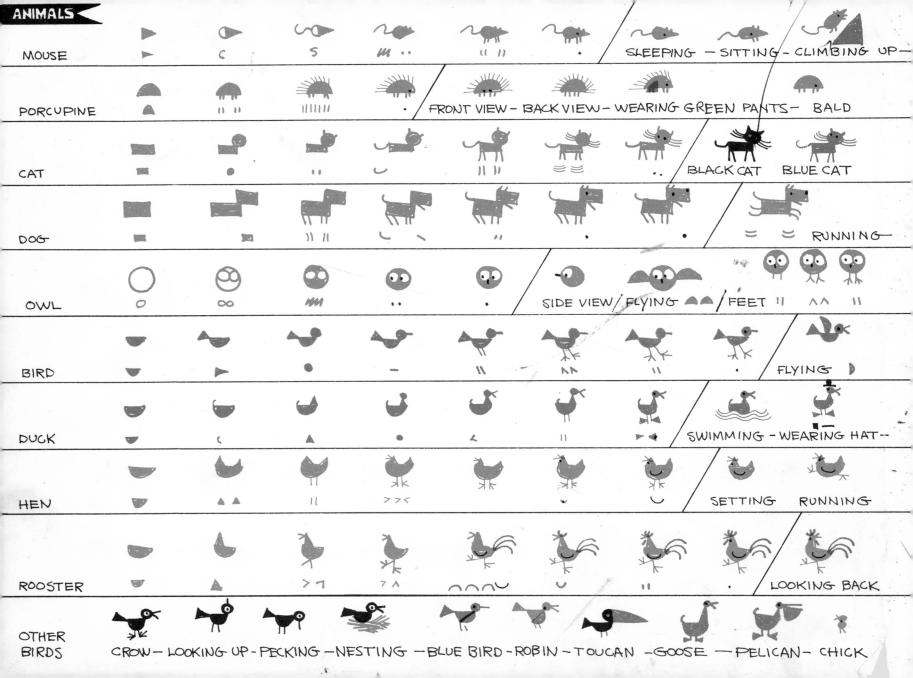

ANIMALS

MOUSE — SLEEPING — SITTING — CLIMBING UP —

PORCUPINE — FRONT VIEW — BACK VIEW — WEARING GREEN PANTS — BALD

CAT — BLACK CAT   BLUE CAT

DOG — RUNNING —

OWL — SIDE VIEW / FLYING / FEET

BIRD — FLYING

DUCK — SWIMMING — WEARING HAT —

HEN — SETTING   RUNNING

ROOSTER — LOOKING BACK

OTHER BIRDS — CROW — LOOKING UP — PECKING — NESTING — BLUE BIRD — ROBIN — TOUCAN — GOOSE — PELICAN — CHICK

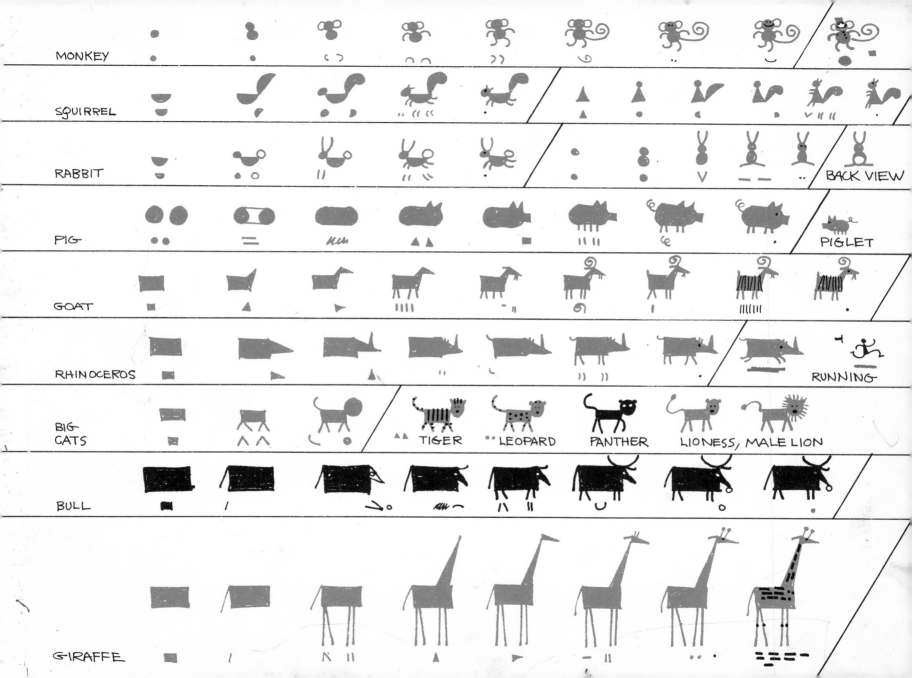

MONKEY

SQUIRREL

RABBIT   BACK VIEW

PIG   PIGLET

GOAT

RHINOCEROS   RUNNING

BIG CATS   TIGER   LEOPARD   PANTHER   LIONESS, MALE LION

BULL

GIRAFFE

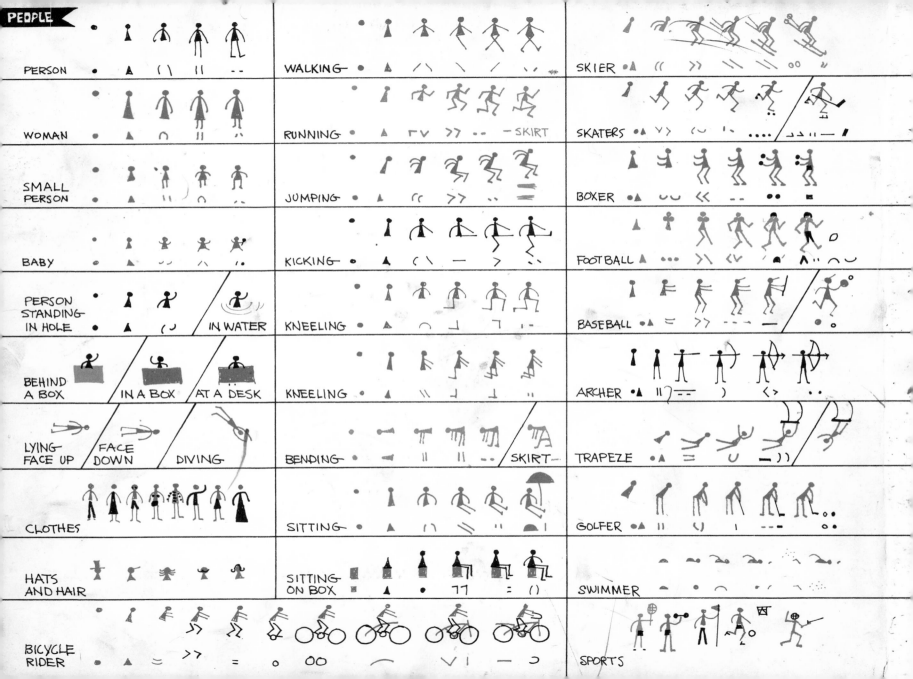

PEOPLE

PERSON

WOMAN

SMALL PERSON

BABY

PERSON STANDING IN HOLE / IN WATER

BEHIND A BOX / IN A BOX / AT A DESK

LYING FACE UP / FACE DOWN / DIVING

CLOTHES

HATS AND HAIR

BICYCLE RIDER

WALKING

RUNNING

JUMPING

KICKING

KNEELING

KNEELING

BENDING / SKIRT

SITTING

SITTING ON BOX

SKIER

SKATERS

BOXER

FOOTBALL

BASEBALL

ARCHER

TRAPEZE

GOLFER

SWIMMER

SPORTS

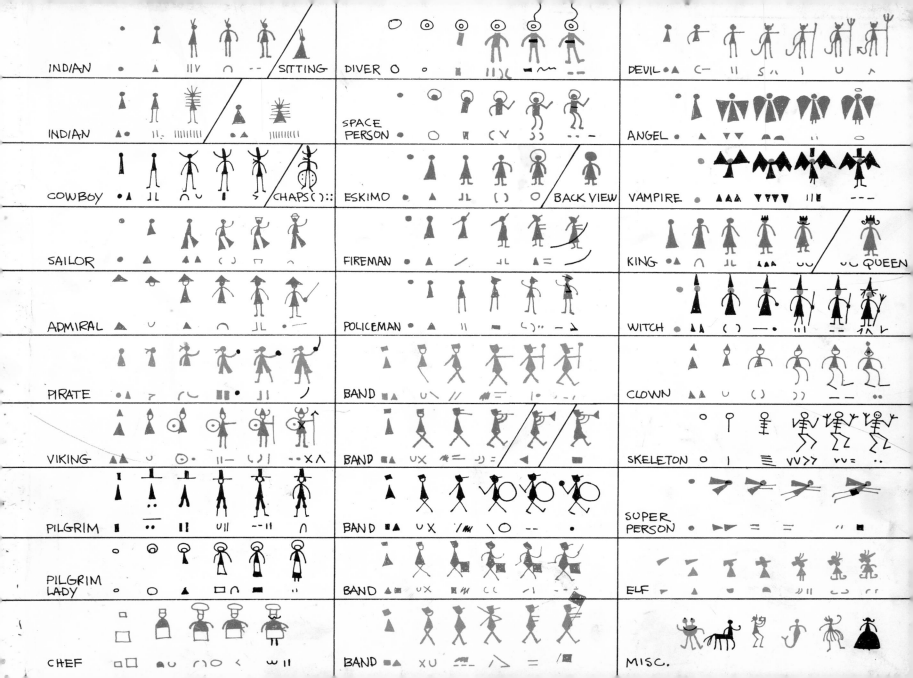

INDIAN | SITTING

INDIAN

COWBOY | CHAPS ( ) ::

SAILOR

ADMIRAL

PIRATE

VIKING

PILGRIM

PILGRIM LADY

CHEF

DIVER

SPACE PERSON

ESKIMO | BACK VIEW

FIREMAN

POLICEMAN

BAND

BAND

BAND

BAND

BAND

DEVIL

ANGEL

VAMPIRE

KING | QUEEN

WITCH

CLOWN

SKELETON

SUPER PERSON

ELF

MISC.

INSIDE STUFF

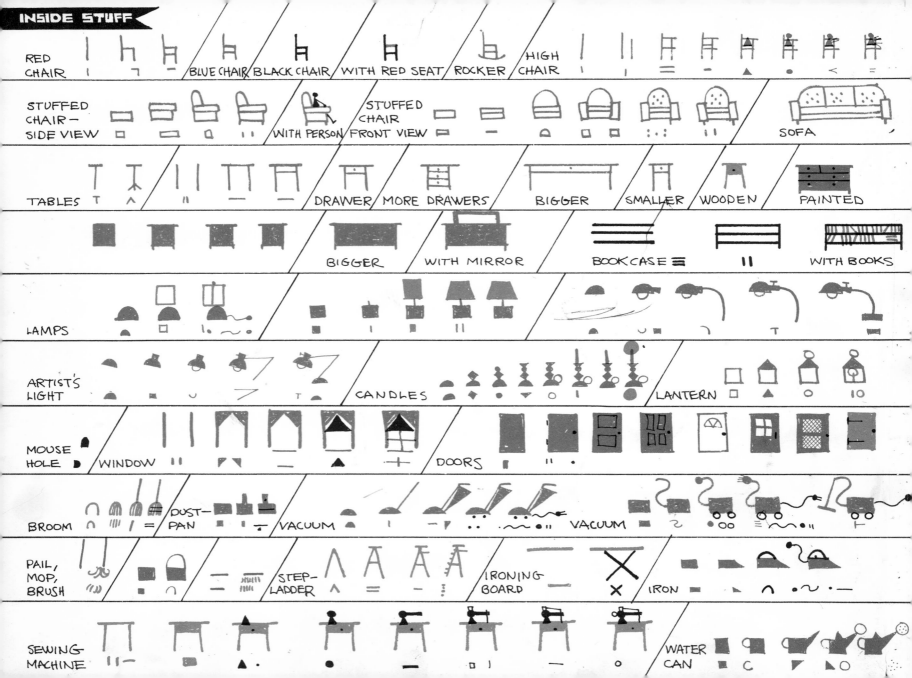

RED CHAIR | BLUE CHAIR | BLACK CHAIR | WITH RED SEAT | ROCKER | HIGH CHAIR

STUFFED CHAIR – SIDE VIEW | WITH PERSON | STUFFED CHAIR FRONT VIEW | SOFA

TABLES | DRAWER | MORE DRAWERS | BIGGER | SMALLER | WOODEN | PAINTED

BIGGER | WITH MIRROR | BOOKCASE | WITH BOOKS

LAMPS

ARTIST'S LIGHT | CANDLES | LANTERN

MOUSE HOLE | WINDOW | DOORS

BROOM | DUST-PAN | VACUUM | VACUUM

PAIL, MOP, BRUSH | STEP-LADDER | IRONING BOARD | IRON

SEWING MACHINE | WATER CAN

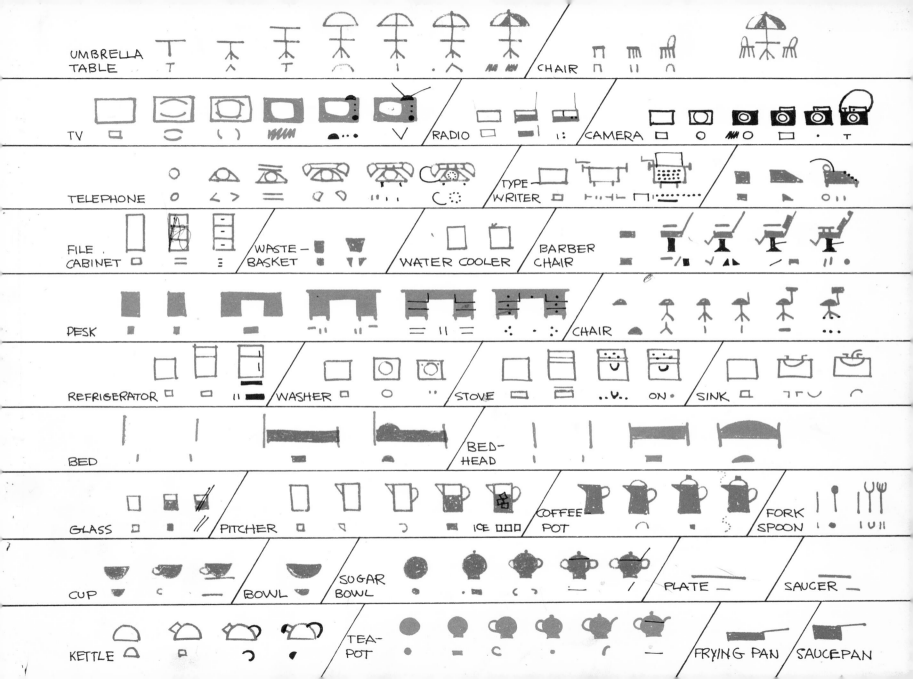

UMBRELLA TABLE

CHAIR

TV

RADIO

CAMERA

TELEPHONE

TYPE WRITER

FILE CABINET

WASTE-BASKET

WATER COOLER

BARBER CHAIR

DESK

CHAIR

REFRIGERATOR

WASHER

STOVE

ON

SINK

BED

BED-HEAD

GLASS

PITCHER

ICE

COFFEE POT

FORK SPOON

CUP

BOWL

SUGAR BOWL

PLATE

SAUCER

KETTLE

TEA-POT

FRYING PAN

SAUCEPAN

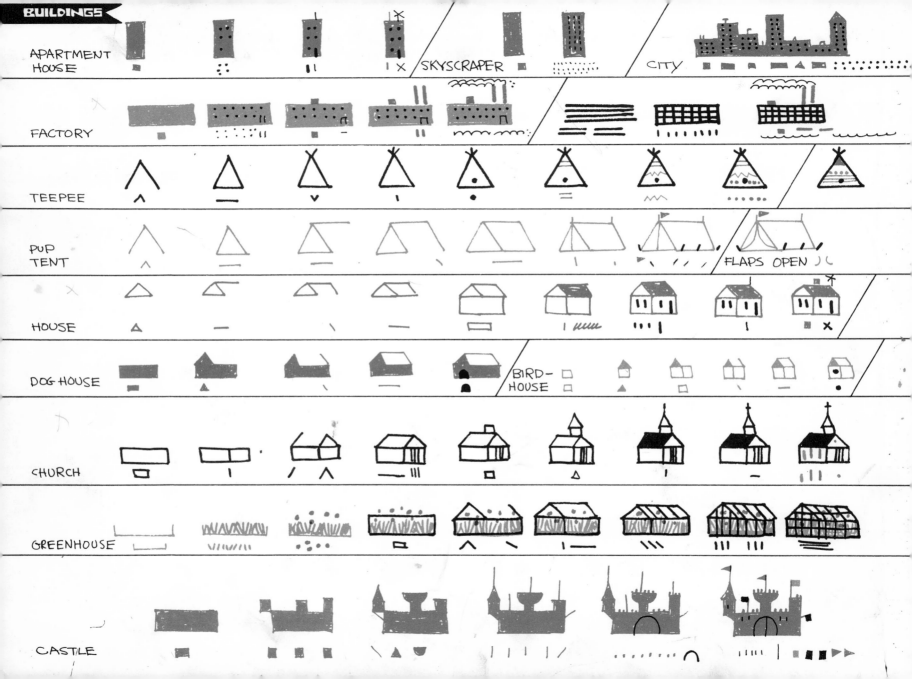

BUILDINGS

APARTMENT HOUSE

SKYSCRAPER

CITY

FACTORY

TEEPEE

PUP TENT

FLAPS OPEN

HOUSE

DOG HOUSE

BIRD-HOUSE

CHURCH

GREENHOUSE

CASTLE

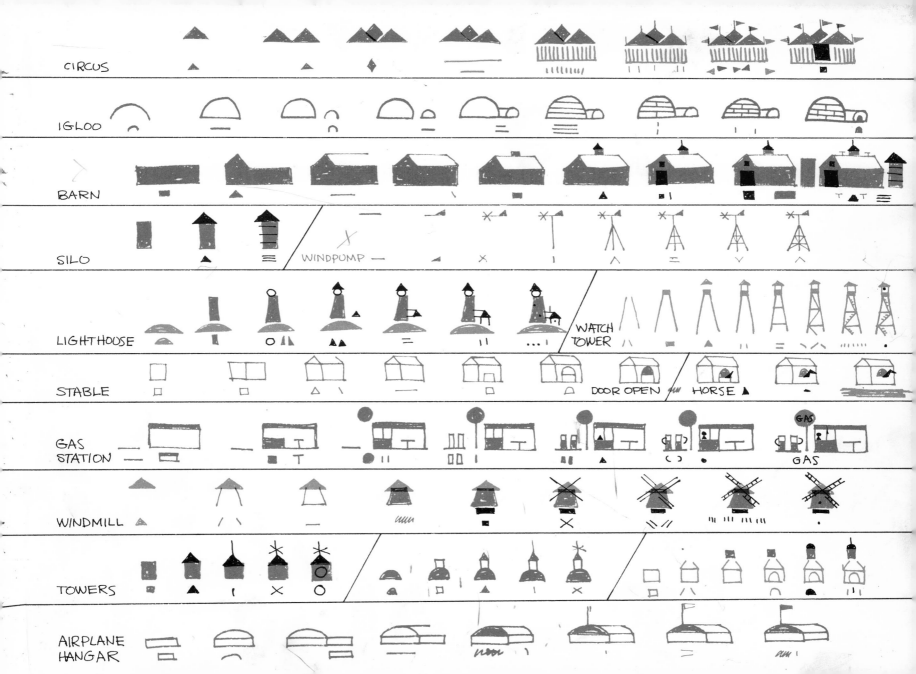

CIRCUS

IGLOO

BARN

SILO WINDPUMP

LIGHTHOUSE WATCH TOWER

STABLE DOOR OPEN HORSE

GAS STATION GAS GAS

WINDMILL

TOWERS

AIRPLANE HANGAR

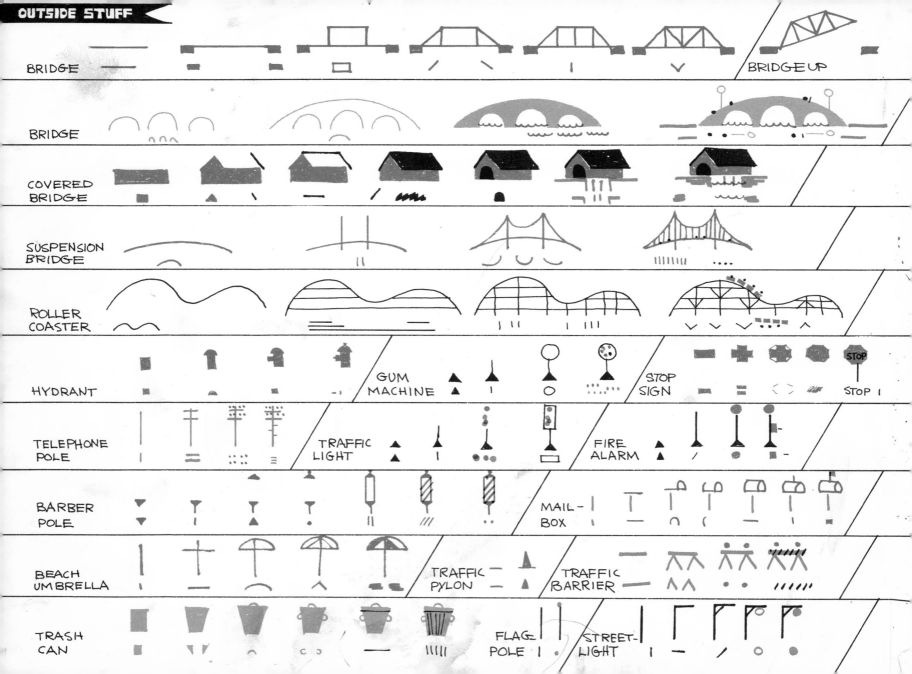

BRIDGE

BRIDGE UP

BRIDGE

COVERED BRIDGE

SUSPENSION BRIDGE

ROLLER COASTER

HYDRANT

GUM MACHINE

STOP SIGN

STOP 1

TELEPHONE POLE

TRAFFIC LIGHT

FIRE ALARM

BARBER POLE

MAIL- BOX

BEACH UMBRELLA

TRAFFIC PYLON

TRAFFIC BARRIER

TRASH CAN

FLAG POLE

STREET- LIGHT

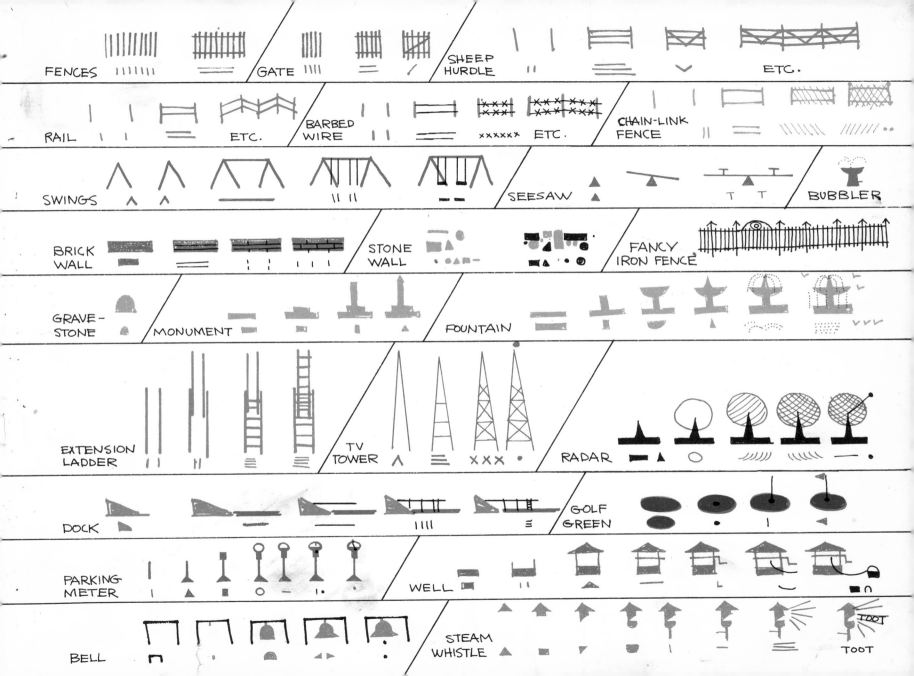

FENCES

GATE

SHEEP HURDLE

ETC.

RAIL

ETC.

BARBED WIRE

ETC.

CHAIN-LINK FENCE

SWINGS

SEESAW

BUBBLER

BRICK WALL

STONE WALL

FANCY IRON FENCE

GRAVE-STONE

MONUMENT

FOUNTAIN

EXTENSION LADDER

TV TOWER

RADAR

DOCK

GOLF GREEN

PARKING METER

WELL

BELL

STEAM WHISTLE

TOOT

TOOT

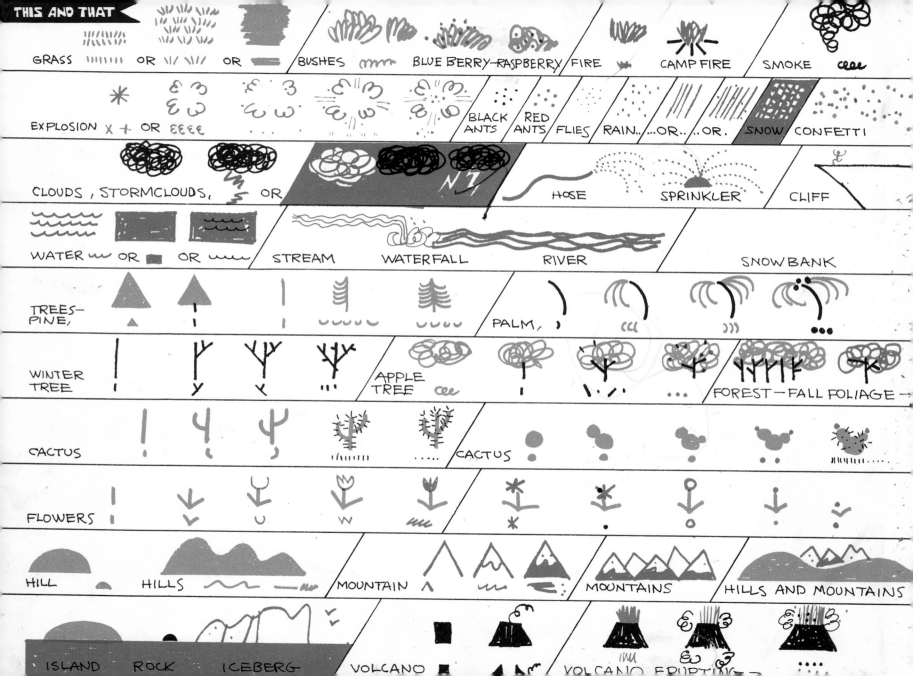

THIS AND THAT

GRASS ||||||| OR \|/ \|/ OR ▬   BUSHES ᵐᵐ   BLUE BERRY · RASPBERRY   FIRE   CAMP FIRE   SMOKE ℓℓ

EXPLOSION X + OR ƐƐƐƐ   BLACK ANTS   RED ANTS   FLIES   RAIN...   ...OR...   ...OR.   SNOW   CONFETTI

CLOUDS , STORMCLOUDS, OR   N I   HOSE   SPRINKLER   CLIFF

WATER ᵂᵂ OR ▪ OR ᵂᵂᵂ   STREAM   WATERFALL   RIVER   SNOW BANK

TREES- PINE,   PALM,

WINTER TREE   APPLE TREE ℓℓ   FOREST — FALL FOLIAGE —

CACTUS   CACTUS

FLOWERS

HILL   HILLS   MOUNTAIN ∧   MOUNTAINS   HILLS AND MOUNTAINS

ISLAND   ROCK   ICEBERG   VOLCANO   VOLCANO ERUPTING —

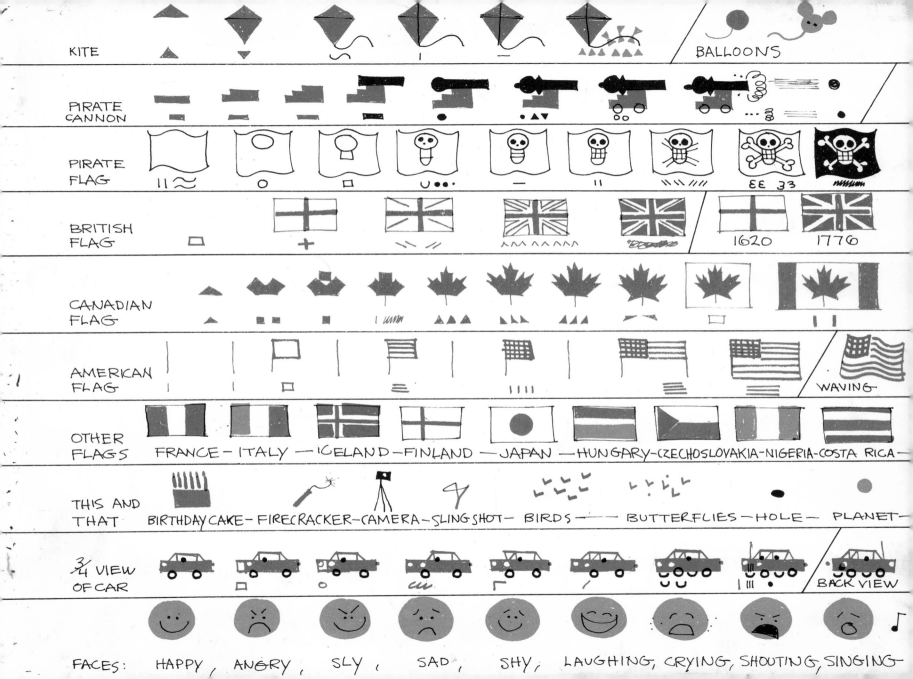

KITE

BALLOONS

PIRATE CANNON

PIRATE FLAG

BRITISH FLAG

1620 1776

CANADIAN FLAG

AMERICAN FLAG

WAVING

OTHER FLAGS

FRANCE — ITALY — ICELAND — FINLAND — JAPAN — HUNGARY — CZECHOSLOVAKIA — NIGERIA — COSTA RICA —

THIS AND THAT

BIRTHDAY CAKE — FIRECRACKER — CAMERA — SLING SHOT — BIRDS — BUTTERFLIES — HOLE — PLANET —

3/4 VIEW OF CAR

BACK VIEW

FACES: HAPPY, ANGRY, SLY, SAD, SHY, LAUGHING, CRYING, SHOUTING, SINGING

✳ HERE ARE SOME OF THE THINGS
YOU CAN DO WITH YOUR PICTURES...

COMIC STRIPS...

POSTERS...

PATTERNS...

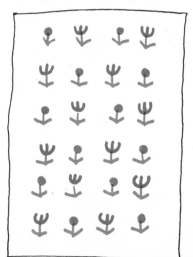

BORDERS...

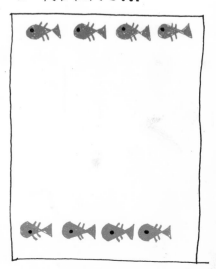

BOOKS....

GOOD KNIGHT

ONCE UPON A TIME...

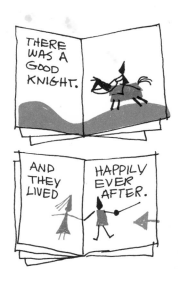
THERE WAS A GOOD KNIGHT.

HE FOUGHT THE DRAGON

AND THEY LIVED HAPPILY EVER AFTER.

MOBILES...

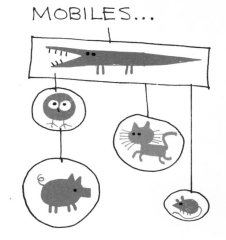

SIGNS...

KEEP OUT

WELCOME

CARDS...

BON VOYAGE

GREETINGS

LETTERS...

DEER ANNE:

HAVING FUN AT CAMP— WISH YOU WERE HERE.

SUE

GAMES, ETC...

PIN THE TAIL ON THE DRAGON

*THERE ARE MANY WAYS
THE DRAWINGS IN THIS BOOK AND YOUR OWN DRAWINGS
CAN BE PUT TOGETHER, ADDED TO OR CHANGED
TO MAKE SOME WORLDS OF YOUR OWN.
FOR INSTANCE...